TECHNIQUE

3A

A COURSE FOR PIANO STUDY

By

LYNN FREEMAN
OLSON

LOUISE
BIANCHI

MARVIN
BLICKENSTAFF

CARL FISCHER®
65 Bleecker Street, New York, NY 10012

O4923

ISBN 0-8258-3384-1

Foreword

Each of the Technique books of **MUSIC PATHWAYS** is divided into three sections:

Finger Drills	to develop finger independence and strength
Technical Skills	to develop scale, chord, and arpeggio facility; hand independence; and pedaling
Etudes	studies from the repertoire

It is suggested that the student be assigned exercises from two or from all three sections concurrently.

Furthermore, the exercises in TECHNIQUE 3A are correlated with the technical problems encountered in REPERTOIRE 3A. A chart showing that correlation is on page 3. The student should be assigned the technical exercise as preparation for his study of the repertoire selection.

Correlation Chart

Compositions in REPERTOIRE 3A	Page	Exercises in TECHNIQUE 3A	Page
Bach, Notebook for Anna Magdalena			
Bourrée	5	expansion and contraction	8
Minuet in G Major	6	5-finger drill	4
		crossings	6
		hand independence	13
		independent voices	16
Bartók			
Imitation and Inversion	27	imitation	13
Staccato and Legato	27	staccato and legato control	8, 9
Beethoven			
Russian Folk-Song	14	crossings	6
		extensions	8
		2-note slurs	9
Duncombe			
Sonatina	8	5-finger drill	4
		contractions	6, 8
Gurlitt			
Dance	20	5-finger drill	4
		trill figure	9
		hand independence	13
Playing Tag	21	imitation	13
		chord shapes	15
Hook			
Minuetto	9	5-finger drill	4
		crossings	6
Hummel			
Theme and Variations	12	5-finger drill	4
		hand independence	13
Kabalevsky			
Follow the Leader	24	staccato 5-finger patterns	8
		imitation	13
Galloping	26	5-finger extensions	5
		staccato, legato control	9
Lively Dance	25	chord shapes	14
Melody	23	hand independence	13
Song	25	5-finger drill	4
		5-finger extensions	5
Lynes			
Sonatina	15	crossings	6
		contractions	8
		trill figure	9
		scales	12, 16
		chord shapes	14, 15
Rebikov			
The Bear	22	double thirds	7
		staccato octaves	8
Siegmeister			
March	30	staccato thirds	7
Tansman			
Arabia	28	5-finger extensions	5
Both ways	29	crossings	6
Telemann			
Gavotte	4	5-finger drill	4
		crossings	6
Türk			
Arioso	10	2-note slurs	9
		hand independence	13
		descending scales	16
Hunting Horns with Echo	11	crossings	6
		chord shapes	15

FINGER DRILLS

These exercises help develop strong fingers and hands.

- repeat each exercise several times
- transpose into other 5-finger positions

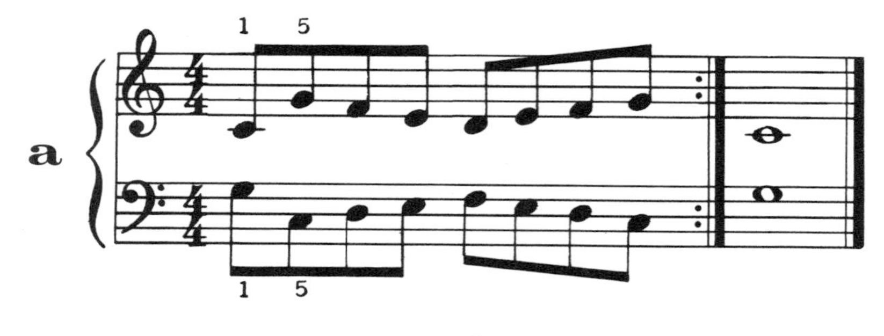

Keys in which you practice these exercises

1. C	6. ____
2. ____	7. ____
3. ____	8. ____
4. ____	9. ____
5. ____	10. ____

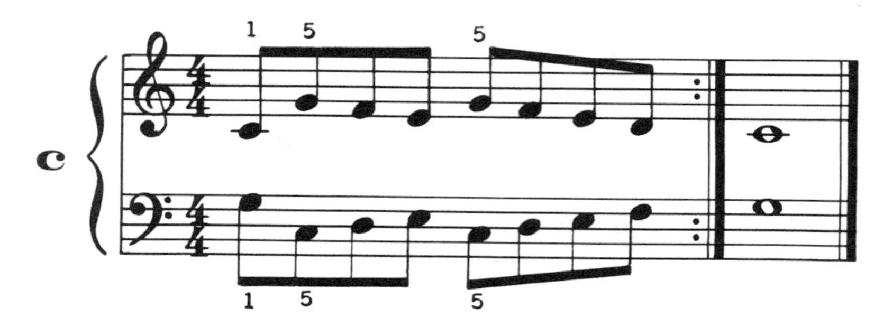

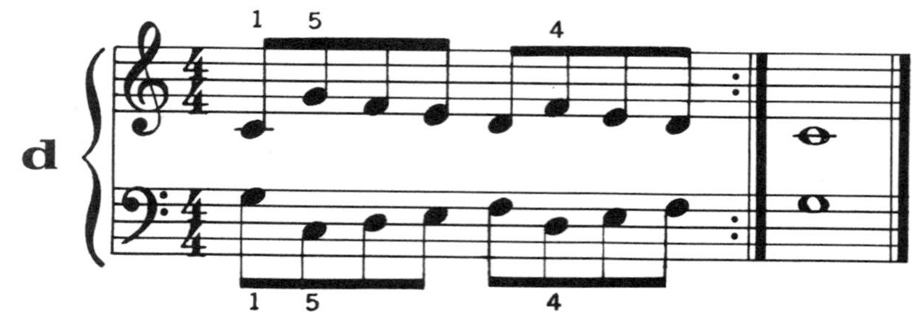

- play *f* with curved fingers
- play *p* with a very smooth sound

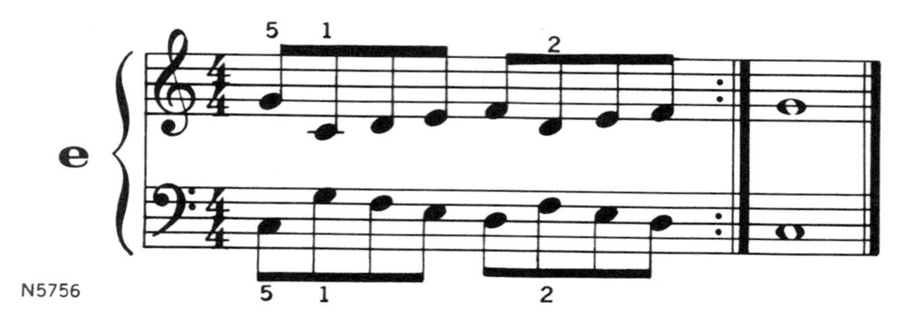

This exercise progresses up and down the keyboard because of the skipped key in each position.

Mister Hanon

- practice the exercise in G Major
  in F Major

3+4

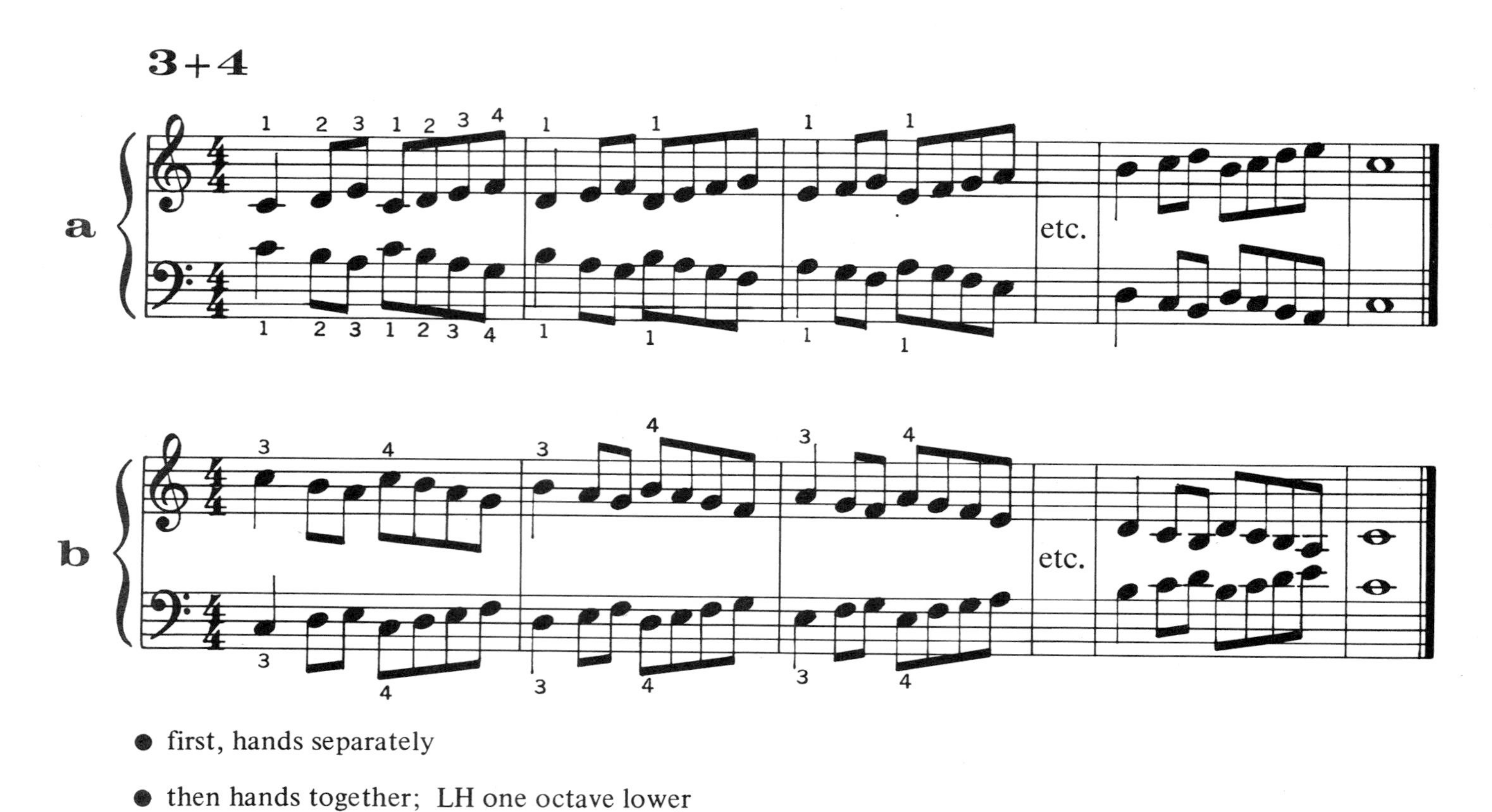

- first, hands separately
- then hands together; LH one octave lower

As your thumb moves onto a new key, let your hand and arm remain motionless.

Circling the Thumb

- transpose into the keys of G Major A Major D Major E Major

3rds in Variation

Major-Minor-Diminished Exercise

There are many different ways to practice the exercise.
Try some of these variations:

- fingers lifted high off the key for an accented sound
- fingers close to the key for a legato sound
- RH *f* LH *p*
- RH *p* LH *f*
- RH staccato LH legato

Jumping Hurdles

- practice hands separately
- when both parts are well-learned, play hands together

Fingering suggestions for TRILL DRILL I and II:

- trill with 3232
- trill with 4343
- trill with 5454

Trill Drill I

Moderately

Trill Drill II

Moderately

Two-Note Slurs

Carefully

TECHNICAL SKILLS

All Major and minor scales are fingered in alternating patterns of

1 2 3   1 2 3 4   1 2 3   1 2 3 4

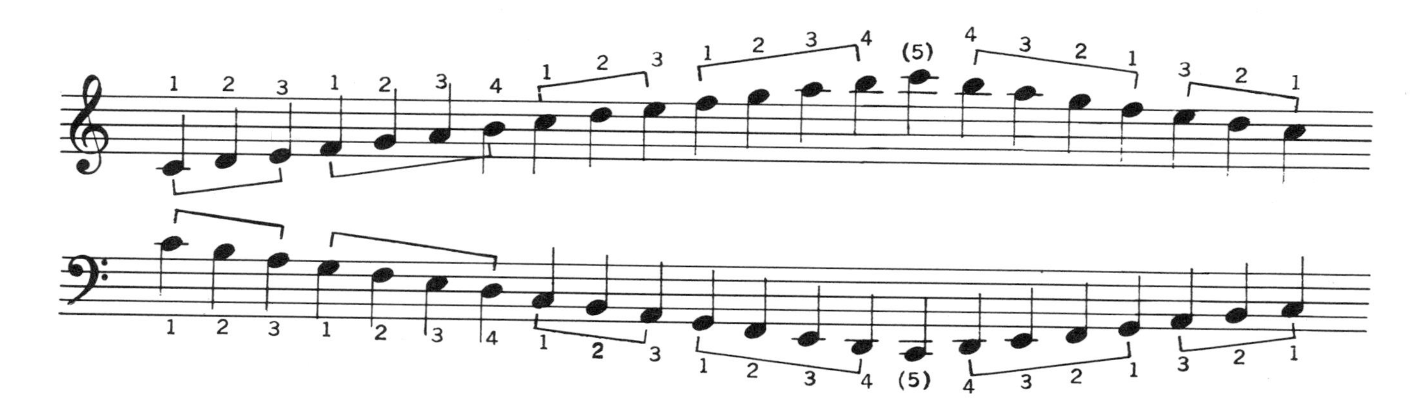

Notice that finger 4 plays only once within an octave scale.

The scales of C, G, D, A, and E are fingered alike. That fingering is given in Rule I.

RULE I: The 4th finger plays next to the keynote (Tonic).

C Major

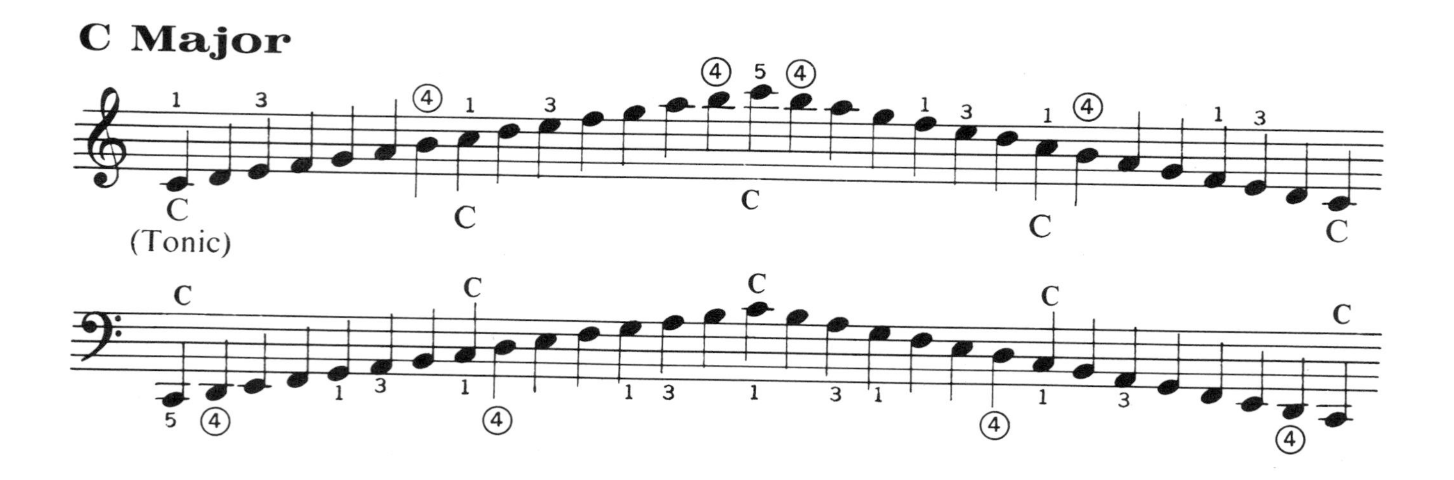

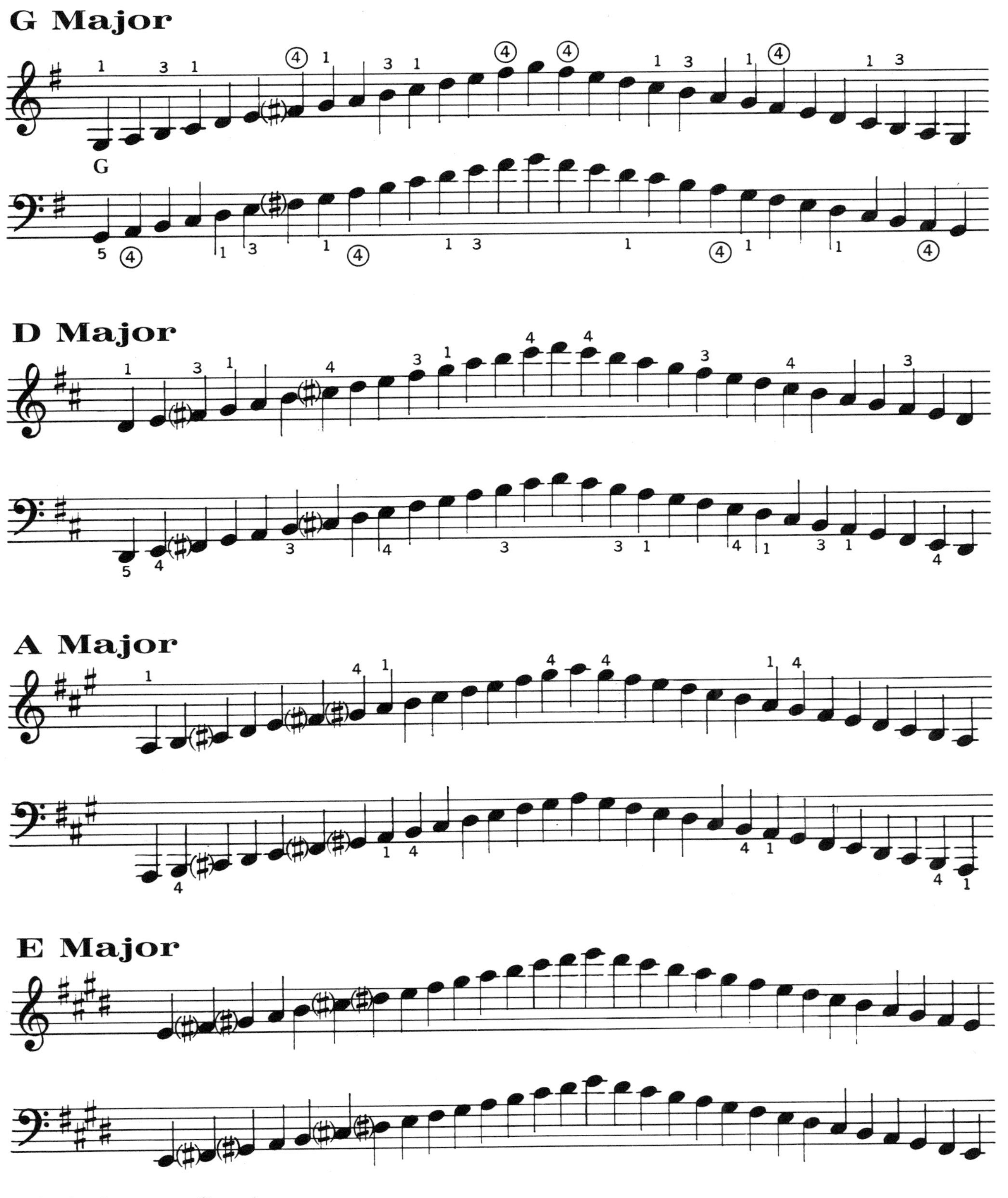

Write in the proper fingering.

In the scales above, do the 4th fingers play next to the Tonic?

Learn to play Rule I Scales, hands separately, from memory.

When playing Rule I scales hands together, which fingers of the same number *always* play together?

This is an exercise to help you play Rule I scales hands together.

Notice that 3's always play together.

Yes, It's 3

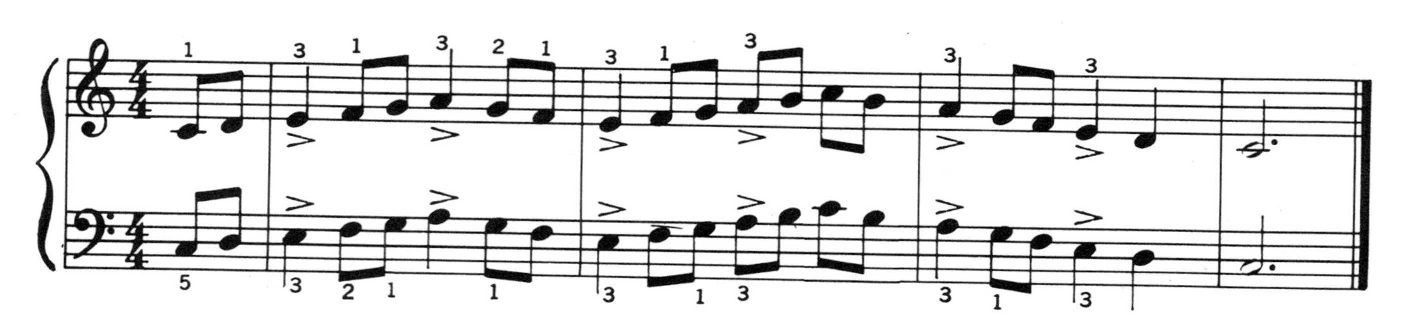

- practice the exercise in all Rule I keys

Rule I check list:

C Major _____ G Major _____ D Major _____ A Major _____ E Major ____

N5756

Indecision

In how many different Major-minor patterns can you play *Indecision?*

Follow the Blind Mouse

Chord Playing

Fingering Guide for Triad Positions

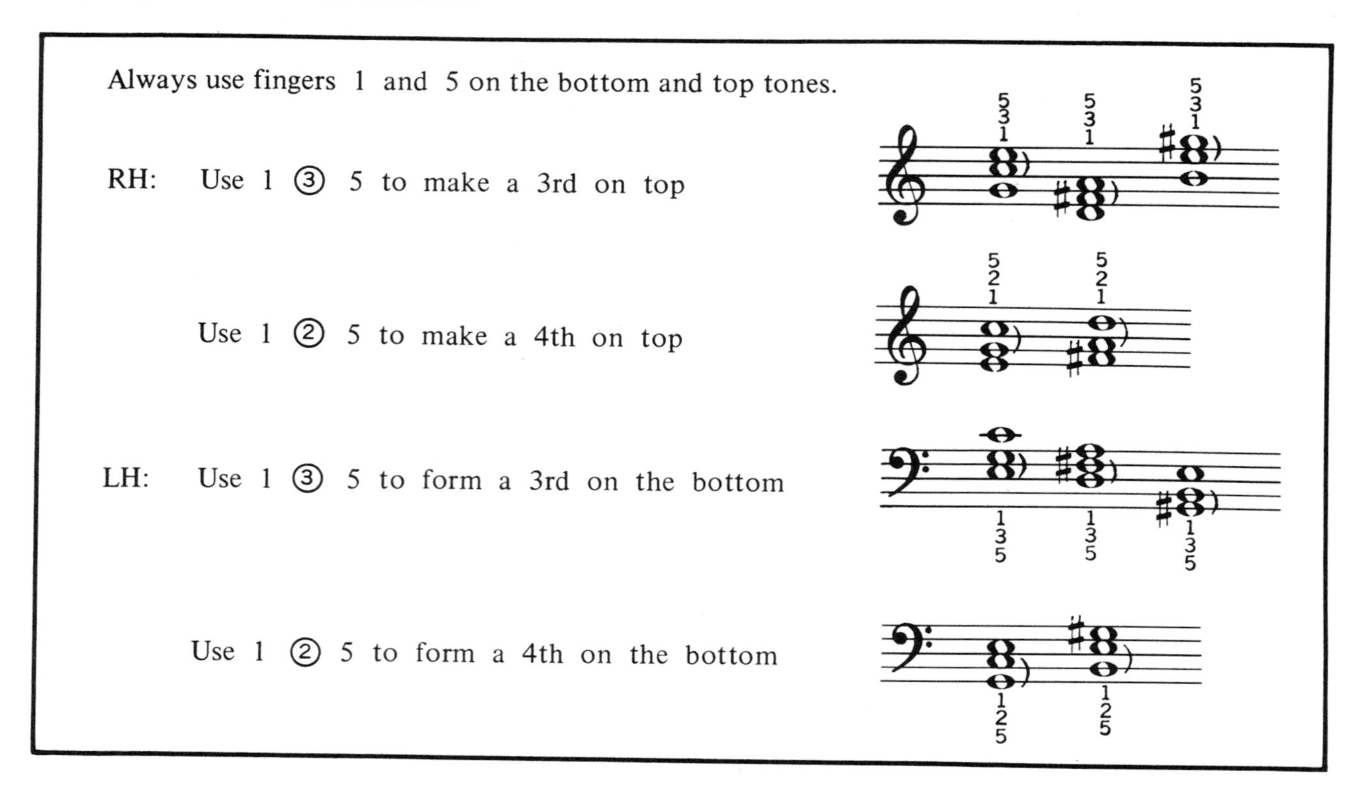

Always use fingers 1 and 5 on the bottom and top tones.

RH: Use 1 ③ 5 to make a 3rd on top

Use 1 ② 5 to make a 4th on top

LH: Use 1 ③ 5 to form a 3rd on the bottom

Use 1 ② 5 to form a 4th on the bottom

As you play from one chord position to the next, watch for the two triad tones which are repeated.

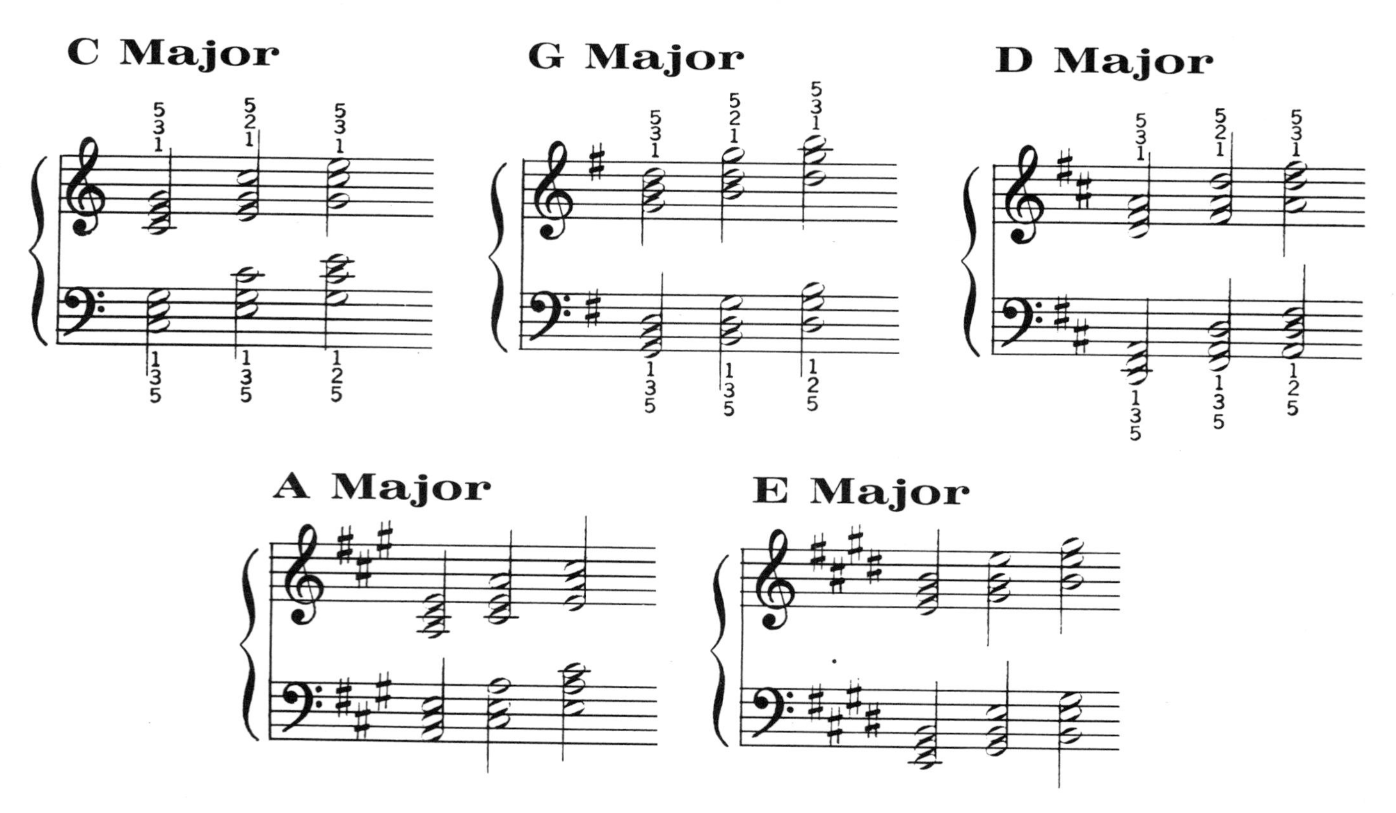

For strength and security in chord playing, keep a good arch in your hand and play on your finger tips.

Broken Chords

Practice these broken chord shapes using the C, G, D, A, and E Major chords.

- hands separately, LH one octave lower than written
- hands together, LH one octave lower than written
- legato
- staccato
- *f*
- *p*

Harp-eggio

Notice the familiar chord shapes in each hand.

Transpose *Harp-eggio* into G, D, A, and E Majors.

ETUDES

Etude in F

Cornelius Gurlitt

Con moto

Etude in A minor

Cornelius Gurlitt

Allegretto